The Apple Tree

By Ruth Corrin

It is winter.
Outside the kitchen window,
the apple tree looks dead.

2

But it isn't dead.
It's just waiting for spring.

3

In spring the tree will grow again.
Tiny buds will cover all its branches.

4

The buds will open
into little white flowers.
Bees will come buzzing.

Then leaf buds will grow.
The flowers will drop their petals.

White petals will flutter down
outside the window.
They will lie on the ground like snow.

Then the leaves will change the tree
to green.

Flowers, with their petals gone,
will slowly change
into little green apples.

All summer the apple tree
will shade the kitchen with its leaves.

The sun will shine,
and the apples will grow and turn red.

When they are ripe,
we'll climb the tree and pick them.

12

The apples will taste good.
But we won't eat them all.

When winter comes again,
we'll still have some left
here in the kitchen—

enough to make an apple pie!